GOOD NEWS!

S0-BZE-076

For almost a year the editors of MAD have been deluged by requests. Every day brings thousands of mailbags ... vast flocks of carrier-pigeons (many of them so heavily loaded they have to come up in the elevator) ... and at night the relentless pounding, pounding, pounding of jungle drums. Now, in answer to this avalanche of anxious requests, we are able to bring you good news!

DOCTOR LIVINGSTONE HAS BEEN FOUND!

He has been right here in the MAD offices all the time! Once that was settled, the editors wanted to celebrate with a new book. They have called it INSIDE MAD (in honor of the happy event) and it includes such amazing features as MICKEY RODENT! (a chilling tale of revenge), MOVIE ADS (fearless-type exposé), SMILIN' MELVIN!, THE KATCHANDHAMMER KIDS!, startling new facts about BAT BOY AND RUBIN!, fascinating PUZZLE PAGES, and much, much more!

Now the editors are relaxed again. They are contented (see picture below). They are happy and well fed. Only trouble is, once again Dr. Livingstone is missing.

THE MAD READER

MAD STRIKES BACK!

and now . . .

CAW!
CAW! CAW!

ALBANY OR BUST

S.S. H.M.S. N.O.A.P.S.

INSIDE
MAD

written by
HARVEY KURTZMAN

drawn by
JACK DAVIS
BILL ELDER
WALLACE WOOD

with a special Backword by
STAN FREBERG

ibooks
new york
www.ibooksinc.com

DISTRIBUTED BY SIMON & SCHUSTER, INC

Original contents copyright © 1953, 1954, 1955
All new material copyright © 2002
E.C. Publications, Inc.

Original cover art copyright 1953, 1954, 1955
New cover design copyright © 2002
E.C. Publications, Inc.

An ibooks, inc. Book

All rights reserved, including the right to reproduce this book
or portions thereof in any form whatsoever.
Distributed by Simon & Schuster, Inc.
1230 Avenue of the Americas, New York, NY 10020

ibooks, inc.
24 West 25th Street
New York, NY 10010

The ibooks World Wide Web Site Address is:
http://www.ibooksinc.com

Visit www.madmag.com

ISBN 0-7434-4480-9
First ibooks, inc. printing May 2002
10 9 8 7 6 5 4 3 2 1

Printed in the U.S.A.

CONTENTS

INTRODUCTION
by Grant Geissman

This book is a facsimile reprint of *Inside MAD*, the third in a new series of 50th-anniversary reprints—published by ibooks—of the early *MAD* paperbacks.

The original version of *Inside MAD* (released in December 1955 by Ballantine Books) followed *The MAD Reader* and *MAD Strikes Back!* (also available in facsimile editions from ibooks). Tracing the successful formula of its antecedents, it featured reformatted material that originally appeared in the twenty-three-issue run of the *MAD* comic book. As before, all of the material was written (and laid out for the artists) by *MAD* creator Harvey Kurtzman, and featured the core group of early *MAD* artists that included Wallace Wood, Jack Davis, and Bill Elder. Like *The MAD Reader* and *MAD Strikes Back!*, *Inside MAD* was a hit upon publication. Ballantine went back to press with the book in January 1956, and additional printings of it were ordered at approximately yearly intervals through 1964.

Continuing the practice of having well-known personalities contribute introductions to the *MAD* books (Roger Price wrote the foreword for *The MAD Reader* and Bob and Ray did the foreword for *MAD Strikes Back!*), Stan Freberg was enlisted to write the introduction for *Inside MAD*. Freberg was then enjoying great success with a series of comedy records (released on Capitol), including

"John and Marsha" (which consisted entirely of the words "John" and "Marsha" uttered at varying emotional levels) and "St. George and the Dragonet," a parody of the TV show *Dragnet*. Interestingly, Kurtzman had also taken on *Dragnet* as an object of satire (Kurtzman's parody, entitled "Dragged Net!," appears in the first volume in this series, *The MAD Reader*). This was hardly surprising; although the two satirists worked in different mediums, they were clearly on the same wavelength.

The opening slot in *Inside MAD* is occupied by "Mickey Rodent!," Kurtzman's look at Walt Disney's most enduring character, Mickey Mouse (*MAD* #19, January 1955, illustrated by Bill Elder). "Mickey Rodent" finds Kurtzman taking on the rivalry between Mickey Mouse and Donald Duck. Elder is at the peak of his game here; his aping of the Disney "house style" is deadly accurate. Elder's "signs in the background" technique is again in evidence, although in this case it's hard to tell where Kurtzman left off and Elder stepped in—signs that specifically advance the story are likely Kurtzman's. As Kurtzman develops his story, "Darnold" begins to smell a rat. Discussing "Mickey Rodent!," Kurtzman told comics historian John Benson that "in choosing my material, my starting point is within some popular subject where I detect a flaw or untruth. You recall when I did the thing on Walt Disney and Mickey Mouse—the three-fingered hand, the white gloves . . . it's a flaw in the sense that the public is accepting a three-fingered thing with white gloves. After all, let's not forget that Mickey Mouse is a huge, upright talking mouse, bigger than a giant rat." Note that at the very end of the piece, it takes but a single panel for Kurtzman to deconstruct Disney's entire anthropomorphic universe!

"Slow Motion!" originally appeared in a much longer form in *MAD* #21 (March 1955, illustrated by Jack Davis). Not only is the story truncated for its appearance here, but the opening panel has been reconfigured: in the original, a golfer is shown standing between the two cameramen, and the skier who appears in this version is not present (the ski image was taken from another panel in the story). "Slow Motion" is one of Kurtzman's "side by side" comparisons, this one showing the difference between what the naked eye sees and what the "slow motion" camera reveals.

Another of Kurtzman's "side by side" comparisons can be found in "Movie . . . Ads!" (*MAD* #14, August 1954, illustrated by Wallace Wood), which compares how scenes in movies are amplified to make them seem more exciting in the print advertising.

"Howdy Dooit!" (*MAD* #18, December 1954, illustrated by Bill Elder) takes on one of the best known and most beloved children's television shows of the 1950s, *Howdy Doody*. The show began on NBC on December 27, 1947, as *Puppet Playhouse with Howdy Doody*, and ran until 1960. The series spawned a merchandising bonanza, including such spin-off items as records, dolls, games, T-shirts, dishware, and even a popular comic book. Hosted by Buffalo Bob Smith (whose moniker came from his birthplace of Buffalo, New York) with his sidekick Clarabell the Clown and a cast of other recurring characters, the show also featured live commercials for the show's sponsors, Hostess Twinkies and Wonder Bread. Such direct advertising to impressionable children was later made illegal, and Kurtzman proves himself to be ahead of the curve here, inserting wry commentary on such practices throughout the story. Elder's art is nothing less than inspired, with his adorable-looking "Peanut Gallery" and endless background details. Note the "Less Work for Mother" tattoo on the arm of the "Peanut Gallery" handler in the second panel of page 45. Apart from the very first panel, in which the television set and the "Howdy Dooit!" lettering was in color (but not the image on the set), the story originally appeared in the *MAD* comic book in black and white to better simulate the black and white television that was then standard. Note that Kurtzman has also rounded off the edges of the panels to better simulate a television screen. As for the story's ending, it is classic Kurtzmania.

The "Canadian Specific," "Puntiac," and "Beer Belongs" ad parodies scattered throughout this book (*MAD* #22, April 1955) were originally part of a "Special Art Issue" that purported to showcase the life and work of *MAD*'s own Bill "Chicken Fat" Elder. In the issue, Kurtzman divided Elder's "life story" into sections: "The Child!," "The Boy!," "The Young Artist!," "The Commercial Artist!," and "The Old Pro'!" These ad parodies originally appeared in the "Commercial Artist!" section, and are notable in that they foreshadow the work both Kurtzman and Elder would do shortly thereafter in the magazine version of *MAD*.

Similarly, the one-page "Rubber Bubble Kids" (*MAD* #21, March 1955) is actually a small part of a much longer feature entitled "Comic Book Ads!," which spoofed the advertising typically found in the back sections of comic books, including such ads as "How to Hypnotize," "319 Stamps–All Different," and the "Red Ryder Cowboy Carbine." For these, Kurtzman had to look no further than the back pages of the comic books issued by *MAD*'s own publisher, EC Comics.

The charming and clever "Puzzle Page!" feature (*MAD* #19, January 1955, art by Bill Elder) that appears here and there throughout this book was originally part of one con-secutive story (entitled "Puzzle Pages!," under the heading "Filler Dept."), and was reconfigured to suit the needs of the paperback for-mat. "Puzzle Page!" sends up the many such one-page "fillers" that regularly appeared in vintage comic books. Not all of the original "Puzzle Pages!" story is present in this book, howev-er; other parts of this piece appear in *MAD Strikes Back!*, the book that pre-cedes this one in the series.

"Pop Art" version, late 1960s
(Art credit unavailable)

"Smilin' Melvin!" (*MAD* #7, October-November 1953, illustrated by Wallace Wood) is Kurtzman's poke at the aviation/adventure strip *Smilin' Jack*. Created by Zack Mosely in 1933, it chronicled the adventures of Jack Martin, a suave, mustachioed commercial pilot whose routes took him on amazing adventures in faraway, exotic places. Among the cast of characters in the strip was Jack's sidekick Downwind Jaxon, a "chick magnet" whose face was so handsome he was never shown beyond a partial profile (parodied here as "Upwind Johnson"). After a long and successful run, *Smilin' Jack* finally had his last adventure on April 1, 1973.

Art by Robert Grossman (1975)

Another long-running (but now somewhat obscure) adventure strip, *Mark Trail*, gets the Kurtzman treatment in "Mark Trade!" (*MAD* #12, June 1954, illustrated by Jack Davis). Created in 1946 by Ed Dodd, the lead character was a somewhat unlikely one: Mark Trail was a woodsman and outdoor photographer who strove to preserve our forests and natural wildlife. Joined in his adventures by a lovable St. Bernard named Andy (spoofed here as "Sandy"), Trail's sensibilities actually predated the ecology movement by several decades. The specific sequence Kurtzman is lampooning here is one in which Trail was hired by *Woods and Wildlife* magazine to save some beavers in Sundance River County from poachers, and to photograph the process for publication in the magazine.

"Katchandhammer Kids!" (*MAD* #20, February 1955, illustrated by Bill Elder) is Kurtzman's treatment of *The Katzenjammer Kids*, widely regarded as the first true comic strip, and one of the longest-running features of any kind. The strip was created by Rudolph Dirks, and debuted on December 12, 1897. It centered on the antics of two incorrigible twins, Hans and Fritz, their long-suffering German-American Mama, and a cast of characters (Hans and Fritz's victims) that included the Captain—a kind of surrogate father to the boys—and "der Inspector," a truant officer. At the end of *MAD*'s send-up, Kurtzman takes the Kids' antics to their logical conclusion.

Art by Norman Mingo (1976)

"Bat Boy and Rubin!" (*MAD* #8, December 1953-January 1954, superbly rendered by Wallace Wood) is a classic and important early Kurtzman parody of Batman and Robin, and was Kurtzman's second look at characters from the DC Comics stable. *MAD* publisher Bill Gaines had already taken heat from DC's lawyers for Kurtzman's previous parody of a DC character, "Superduperman!" (see *The MAD Reader*), which prompted the "Notice! This story is a lampoon!" disclaimer in "Batboy and Rubin's" splash panel, lest DC again get the wrong idea.

"Shermlock Shomes!" (*MAD* #7, October-November 1953, illustrated by Bill Elder), sends up Sherlock Holmes, the classic and archetypal English detective created in 1887 by Sir Arthur Conan Doyle. Aided by his trusted friend Dr. Watson ("Whatsit"), Holmes's superior deductive abilities inevitably would allow him to outwit his arch enemy Moriarty ("Arty-Morty"). In coining the surname "Shomes" for this parody, Kurtzman was likely combining "Holmes" with "shamus," the Yiddish word for a detective or private eye. The Holmes character provided fertile enough material for Kurtzman to visit a second time in *MAD*; he tackled Doyle's *The Hound of the Baskervilles* (as "Shermlock Shomes in The Hound of the Basketballs") in a later issue of the *MAD* comic book.

It is gratifying (and even a little awe-inspiring) to note that the material that constitutes *Inside MAD*, originally published a scant three years after *MAD* made its debut in 1952 as a 10¢ comic book, is important enough to warrant this special 50th-anniversary edition.

Grant Geissman *is the author of* Collectibly MAD, *(Kitchen Sink Press, 1995), and co-author with Fred von Bernewitz of* Tales of Terror! The EC Companion *(Gemstone/Fantagraphics, 2000). He compiled and annotated the "best of" volumes* MAD About the Fifties *(Little, Brown, 1997),* MAD About the Sixties *(Little, Brown, 1995),* MAD About the Seventies *(Little, Brown, 1996), and* MAD About the Eighties *(Rutledge Hill Press, 1999). He compiled and wrote liner notes for* MAD Grooves *(Rhino, 1996), and also contributed the intro-duction to* Spy vs. Spy: The Complete Casebook *(Watson-Guptill, 2001). When not reading* MAD, *Geissman is a busy Hollywood studio guitarist, composer, and "contem-porary jazz" recording artist with 11 highly regarded albums released under his own name.*

Foremost among the song parodists is a young Californian who has rocked the nation with such hits as "John and Marsha," "Try," and now "Rock and Roll Around Stephen Foster." You've seen his writing in Mad, Colliers and other influential media. Now it gives us great pleasure to present this special Backword by Stan Freberg. Mr. Freberg . . .

Well?

Where is he?

I don't see anybody.

Hold it. HOLD IT! You kids want to read Stan Freberg, don't you? Sure you do! Tell you what you do, then. Stan's Backword is around in the *back* of the book. Let's all turn to page 183 in our MAD books. Got that—page 183. Ready? Start turning!

INSIDE MAD

Animation Dept.: Here is a thought! Who amongst you have seen the sight of man turned beast? A hapless few, we trust! ... And yet ... though we are repelled at the sight of man turned beast ... we revel to see beast turned man! When you pass along this thought ... remember you saw it in MAD! ... And now, our story ...

MICKEY RODENT!

3

5

9

13

15

17

19

21

For a world of service, travel Canadian Specific. Canadian Specific's 4-engined pressurized airliners fly from Canada to Hawaii, Fiji, New Zealand, Australia, Belgian Congo, Tibet, the North Pole, the Kremlin, the Moon and Kukamonga. By George! We take you anywhere! Canadian Specific's engined pressurized airliners have the straightest lines trailing out in back of the airplane drawings in their ads then any other airline.

Canadian Specific

SPANS THE WORLD

Science Dept.: You ever watch one of those sports newsreels where they've sped up the camera to slow down the action? By George, there's more going on than meets the eye!... Like forinstance, let us show you what happens to a ski jumper coming off the end of the jump...as seen by our camera in...

SLOW MOTION!

25

SKIERS ARE PROBABLY CRAZY, BUT WE'VE GOT SO USED TO WATCHING THEM THAT WE THINK NOTHING OF SEEING THE SKIER FLY THROUGH THE AIR AND FALL HUNDREDS OF FEET!

...WE THINK NOTHING OF SEEING HIM LAND IN A BIG FLURRY OF SNOW!... LITTLE DO YOU KNOW WHAT THINGS GO ON IN THAT BIG FLURRY OF SNOW!

THE FURSHLUGGINER SLOW-MOTION CAMERA HAS ALL THE ANSWERS!

...HERE, AFTER DESCENDING, OUR SKIER MAKES CONTACT WITH GROUND...

...THIS PARTICULAR SKIER HAS MADE VERY FAULTY LANDING!

...HERE, SKIER, BE-CAUSE OF FAULTY LANDING, LEAVES GROUND!

...HERE SKIER REACHES APEX OF FIRST BOUNCE AND IS READY TO DESCEND!

28

...NOTE FOR MOMENT WHILE SKIER IS OUT OF PICTURE, DEEP GOUGES IN SNOW!

...NOTE SKIER DESCENDS INTO PICTURE AGAIN, THIS TIME HEAD FIRST!

...NOTE HEAD ABOUT TO CONTACT GROUND WITH GREAT FORCE!

...NOTE FORCE WITH WHICH SNOW AND ROCKS ARE FLUNG FROM IMPACT!

...NOW NOTE SEPARATE PARTS OF SKIER AS THEY BOUNCE UP FOR LAST TIME!

TV Dept.: Our constant readers have no doubt noticed our sudden shift to television! We are giving special attention to TV because we believe it has become an integral part of living . . . a powerful influence in shaping the future . . . but mainly we are giving attention because we just got a new TV set! So here's our story . . .

HOWDY DOOIT!

31

38

39

IT'S NO USE! HE'S ALREADY WHIPPING THOSE THINGS OUT OF THAT BOX!... HERE COMES THE SELTZER BOTTLE!... WE MIGHT AS WELL STAND AND MEET OUR FATE!

...GOSH... WHAT'S GOING TO HAPPEN NEXT? WELL, KIDS! IT'S ME, *HOWDY DOOIT* AGAIN AND THIS TIME I'M ADVERTISING *SKWUSHY'S* SLICED WHITE-BREAD! NOW LISTEN, KIDS... THE NEXT TIME YOUR MOTHER GOES TO THE STORE, I WANT YOU TO ASK HER TO BUY A LOAF OF *SKWUSHY'S!*

HALF - BAKED
WHILE YOU SLEEP!
SKWUSHY'S *
* A WONDER PRODUCT:
"IF IT'S GOOD BREAD-IT'S
A WONDER!"

NOW IN CASE YOUR MOTHER REFUSES TO BUY YOU A LOAF OF *SKWUSHY'S*, HERE'S WHAT TO DO! NOW MAKE BELIEVE I'M YOU AND MAKE BELIEVE THAT'S YOUR MOTHER SHOPPING IN THE SUPERMARKET AND SHE DOESN'T WANT TO BUY BREAD TODAY!

...YOU JUST WAIT TILL HER BACK IS TURNED AND SLIP A LOAF OF SWUSHY'S INTO THE SHOPPING BASKET!...HIDE IT WAY UNDER WHERE SHE CAN'T NOTICE IT!...THEN AGAIN...IF MOM HAPPENS TO BUY ANOTHER BRAND OF BREAD...

ZIP!

...WAIT TILL SHE GETS STUCK ON THE LINE AT THE CASHIER'S COUNTER AND QUICK SUBSTITUTE A LOAF OF *SKWUSHY'S!* SHE'LL *HAVE* TO BUY IT!... BESIDES *SKWUSHY'S* WHITE BREAD, TRY *SKWUSHY'S* GREEN AND PURPLE BREAD!

ZIP!

4

45

DOT PUZZLES

'DOT-PUZZLES', GANG! LOTS OF KEEN FUN AHEAD FOR EVERYONE!

YOU MUST HAVE SEEN THIS FEATURE... HERE ARE TWO CONNECTING-DOT PUZZLES. THE FIRST ONE IS EASY... JUST A STARTER! IF YOU CAN COMPLETE IT, TRY YOUR HAND AT THE NEXT ONE WHICH IS SLIGHTLY MORE DIFFICULT! WHEN YOU GET ALL THE DOTS CONNECTED, THEY MAKE A *PICTURE!* GOSHAROOTIE! THEY CAN BE FRAMED N' EVERYTHING... WHY... *THEY TEACH YOU HOW TO DRAW!* SOME PUZZLE, HUH, GANG?... SOME FEATURE, HUH?

ANSWERS ON LAST PAGE!

51

Dollar for Dollar

You Can't Beat a

PUNTIAC

Famous For Dependability—The World Over!

When you drive a Puntiac Special cross-country, taking hills and mountains as they come . . . exploring little-known byways . . . covering the many miles a day the vast spaces of our big country require—that's when you most appreciate Puntiac Special's big-car performance.

You're easy and relaxed behind that mighty power plant—the most thoroughly proved engine in any car. Police cars are no problem—your Puntiac Special is so nimble and alert. You ride without annoying bullets going past your head. The thick, bullet proof glass takes care of that. You step on the accelerator and pull away from that police car as if it were going in reverse, for Puntiac Special provides the quick-start and pick-up that bank robbers so often need in a pinch.

Sounds good? You'll like this even better when you've covered the many miles a day you require to make your getaway. Puntiac Special is specially priced for bank robbers. And why not. You'll have to rob a bank to pay the price. See your Puntiac dealer today

PUNTIAC DIVISION OF GENERAL MURDERS INCORPORATED

Puntiac Special's trunk space is phenomenal. You can store away a whole arsenal besides a human body. And there'll be plenty of room to spare for your extra suitcases of money.

53

This is the story of the men who go alone into the Wild Blue Yonder . . . the unsung heroes who go fearlessly, not for riches, not for glory . . . into the Wild Blue Yonder . . . some never to return! Ah yes . . . the Wild Blue Yonder Bar and Grill, where we find the hero of our story . . .

SMILIN' MELVIN!

55

57

...THE X-4... THE X-5...X-6...X-7...X-8...X-9, 10, 11, AND THE SECRET-SUPER-TURBO-HYPER-PTOOEY JET *X-12!*... TSK TSK!...LOST *TWELVE GOOD* TEST PILOTS!... NOW, DID YOU SAY YOU *WOULD* FLY THE SECRET-SUPER-TURBO-HYPER PTOOEY-JET *X-13?*

UPWIND!...I ASK YOU AGAIN! ...DO YOU THINK I AM AFRAID?

...NOW I ANSWER MY OWN QUESTION! *...YOU BET!*

P-TEEEEENG!

NOW LISTEN, MELVIN! TAKE MY WORD FOR IT, AS YOUR FRIEND, YOU HAVE NOTHING TO WORRY ABOUT! THERE'S NOTHING WRONG WITH THE X-13! THE X-13 IS A *GOOD SHIP!*

...BUT WHO EVER HEARD OF FLYING A SHIP?

...YUK YUK YUK!...ALL KIDDING ASIDE...I HAVE FULL CONFIDENCE IN YOUR WORD, UPWIND...AND I AM SURE EVERYTHING WILL WORK OUT ALL RIGHT LIKE YOU SAY. BUT BEFORE I DIE..THERE IS *ONE THING I MUST KNOW...ONE THING YOU'VE GOT TO TELL ME, BOY...*

59

63

73

You who love the sound of the sighing forest . . . you who love the sight of the sparkling mountain lake . . . you who love the feel of the squooshing cow pasture . . . you who hoo you hoohoo you! His name was his trade mark . . . his trade mark his name . . . and that's his name . .

77

81

87

93

95

AND AS THEY FADE INTO THE SUNSET, WE END THE STORY OF THE MAN WHOSE NAME WAS HIS TRADE-MARK, HIS TRADE-MARK HIS NAME... AND THAT'S HIS NAME... *MARK TRADE!*

Cinema Dept.: You know how sometimes movie ads give a phony impression?!...like forinstance...take a scene from a typical...

Advertising Dept.: ... So then the Hollywood ad men get ahold of the scene, and here's what you see in the newspapers ...

...GET THE GENERAL IDEA?... LIKE FOR INSTANCE...A WAR PICTURE BEGINS... G.I'S SLOGGING THROUGH THE MUD!

... FOR TEN REELS THEY GO, ALL SHMEARED WITH DIRT AND BEARDS... SLOGGING THROUGH THE MUD!

FINALLY THEY REACH THE ACTION! *BLAM-BLAM!* A ENEMY SOLDIER FALLS OFF A CLIFF! THE *GOOD GUYS* WIN THE HILL!

THE VICTORIOUS G.I.'S MARCH INTO THE LIBERATED TOWN!...FOR TWO SECONDS, A GIRL JUMPS OUT AND KISSES A SOLDIER!

AND THEN THE LIEUTENANT ORDERS THE MEN OUT BECAUSE THERE'S ALWAYS ANOTHER HILL TO CONQUER!

...AND THAT'S THE WAY THE PICTURE ENDS WITH THE G.I.'S SLOGGING OFF THROUGH THE MUD...

...SO AFTER SEEING *ONE* GIRL FOR ONLY *TWO* SECONDS IN A *TWO HOUR PICTURE*... HERE'S THE WAY THE ADVERTISEMENT GOES..

...FINALLY... AN ADVENTURE PICTURE!...THIS GIRL IS SICK SOMEWHERE IN BROOKLYN, SEE? SHE'S NAUSEOUS!

SHE HAS A RARE INCURABLE DISEASE SO SHE GOES TO MIAMI! A PILOT STRUCK BY HER BEAUTY... FALLS...

...OFF THE WING OF HIS PLANE!IT REALLY ISN'T HIS PLANE AND WHEN HE FLIES TO KUKAMONGA, THE REAL OWNER HITS HIM...

PAF

...BECAUSE HE'S SUCH A SLOPPY PILOT! ANYHOW...THE PILOT MEETS THE GIRL AGAIN IN BANFF, AT THE AQUARIUM...

SHE FLEES ON A BOAT TO POONA WHERE HE CATCHES HER AND AS SHE LEANS NAUSEOUS OVER THE RAIL...

...SHE TELLS HIM OF HER INCURABLE DISEASE! HE MARRIES HER ANYHOW! THEY GO TO SEE VESUVIUS ON THEIR HONEYMOON!

THAT'S THE PICTURE!... THE NEWSPAPERS COME OUT WITH RATINGS... LIDDLE STARS, LIDDLE BELLS, LIDDLE HALF-STARS...

...THE AD MEN GET TO WORK! THEY CUT, THEY PASTE, THEY RETOUCH, THEY PUT LIDDLE PIECES TOGETHER...

...THEY MAKE A BIG AD WITH ALL THE EXCITING SCENES MAKING ONE BIG PICTURE. LIKE IT'S ALL ONE SCENE!

MOVIE COLUMN by Curlip Sneary

NEW LOW IN MOVING PICTURES

A collosal time waster was Warndher Bros.' latest release "The Spectacle". What stupendous nerve they had in showing such a picture. It was wonderful to get out of the theater. I was dying looking at this dog and it felt so good to leave when it finally ended. Have never been so...

MOVIES by Ripsaw Teardown

ECHHHHHHH!

Last nite I saw 'The Spectacle'. This is the kind of film I like to see taken out and burned. In fact, that's what I did. I went up to the projection booth, took out the film and burned it! Boy, did I have a wonderful time! And now to another so-called miserable so-called...

The Cinema by Chewup Spitout

RATINGS
★★★★ - excellent
★★★ - good
★★ - medium
★ - cruddy

THE SPECTACLE
1/16 ★

After I saw this film, I went up to the projection booth and killed the projectionist. This is the kind of film for stars to avoid, since it does more harm than good to their career. If this mong ity plays at theater. burn the house do...

...THOUSANDS OF MILES APART, THE SCENES ARE TAKING PLACE...SO THEY MAKE IT ONE SCENE...LIKE THIS...

THIS SCENE WILL STEAM YOUR GLASSES

Starring - VAVA VOW -- Have you met Vava Vow .... the 3-D WHAM girl?

Produced by - HERMAN LENTH   Directed by - MOE BREDTH   Written by MELVIN DEPFTH

Says Movie Columnist
CURLIP SNEARY --

"New... A collossal time...
...stupendous... wonderful...
felt so good ..."

Says critic
RIPSAW TEARDOWN --

" This is the kind of film I
like to see... Boy, did I
have a wonderful time..."

Says writer
CHEWUP SPITOUT --

" *... for stars* ...."
(★ ★ ★ ★)

Newspaper Cartoon Dept.: Today we present two charming boys who for years have been making mischief on such a scale that although it isn't publicized, they have made their home a shambles and laid waste to the land!... Yes... You guessed it!...Those two lovable little rascals, Hans and Feetz...The...

KATCHANDHAMMER KIDS!

113

117

118

ICH HORT GEPUTTEN ON MEIN BESTEN UNIFORM FUR DAS REASON! AT LONGEN LAST, ICH HORT GEGOTTEN EIN OFFER ZU KOMMANDING EIN BOAT! ICH HORT GEWAITING YEARS FUR DAS OPPORTUNITY! DER BOAT KOMPANY IST GESENDING EIN MANN OVER TODAY FUR INTERVIEWEN ME UND ICH GOT ZU MACHEN EIN GUTEN IMPRESSION!

SH! ...WAS IST DAS NOISE?

SKRITCH

EAST ZONE

WEST ZONE

...DAS IST DER LASTEN OPPORTUNITY ICH VILT EVER HABEN ZU BE EIN REAL KAPITAN! ICH HORT ZU MACHEN EIN GUTEN IMPRESSION!

AHA! ICH HORT GETHOUGHT ICH HORT GEHEARD A NOISE IN DEM CLOSET!

...DER KINNDER MACHEN MONKEY BUSINESS! STEPPEN ZIE ASIDE UND ICH OPENEN DER DOOR!

DUN'T FORGET! NO PUTTING CHIKEN FET ON DER STER RALES MAMA.

119

...UBER KAPITAN, IST DU **SURE** DAS IST DER BESTEN IDEA FUR TEACHING DER KINNDER TO BEHAVING? DU HAST GEHEARD VAS SIGMUND FREUD HORT GESPOKEN...

HALTEN MIT DAS BENDEN OF MINE EAREN UND COMEN ZU PLAYING GIN-RUMMY! COMEN ZIE INSIDE!

DAS SHOTTEN DER KINNDER IN DER KISHKERS IST GONNA GEMACHEN EIM SEHR WORSE! WASS DER KINNDER NEED IST DER LITTLE GELOVING UND LIKE DAS!

...UBER BEFORE ICH GERINGEN DOORBELL... ICH GEGOING TO PUTTEN ON DAS RUBBER GLOVES FUR INSULATION FRUM DAS ELECTRICITEN SHOCK!

KAPITAN! KAPITAN! WAS IST LOS?

GOTTEN HIMMEL! DAS FURSHLUGGINER DOORBELL AIN'T HABEN ELECTRICITEN SHOCK.! DAS TIME IT HABEN POINTY NEEDLE STICKEN OUT!

131

133

"PLAYING CROQUET ON THE FRONT LAWN," by Bill Elder. Number 1 in the series "Booze Life in America."

Beer and ale— mealtime favorites

In this friendly, freedom-loving land of ours—*beer belongs ... enjoy it!*

AMERICA'S BEVERAGE OF MODERATION

Sponsored by the Brewer's Foundation to Encourage Excess

Hero Worship Dept.: You have heard of those two masked batlike crime fighters of Gotham City. . . . You have heard of their exciting deeds, of their constant war against the underworld! . . . This story, then . . . This story, then . . . has *absolutely nothing* to do with them! This story is about two different people. . . .

BAT BOY AND RUBIN!

149

153

WHAT'S WRONG WITH THIS PICTURE?

HAVING FUN, GANG?... BET YOU ARE... MAINLY SINCE THIS IS THE LAST NAUSEATING PAGE IN THIS PUZZLE-PAGE FIASCO! IN THE FOLLOWING PICTURES, THE ARTIST HAS MADE A NUMBER OF MISTAKES! SEE IF YOU CAN FIND AND LIST THEM!... NEEDLESS TO SAY, THE ARTIST WILL BE FIRED AS PROMPTLY AS POSSIBLE SINCE THIS COMPANY DOES VERY GOOD, HIGH-CLASS ART WORK USING ONLY THE BEST AND WE KICK OUT ALL ARTISTS WHO MAKE MISTAKES!

WHAT'S WRONG WITH THIS PICTURE?

ANSWERS ON LAST PAGE!

A fog lies thick on London, giving a lonely, eerie quality to the night sounds! . . . The ominous chiming of Big Ben . . . the footsteps of some*thing* scuttling by . . . the hollow clack of Dr. Whatsit's head coming in contact with a lamppost as he rushes through the fog to see his old friend . . .

SHERMLOCK SHOMES!

160

161

163

171

173

177

179

181

ANSWER PAGE
BILL ELDER DREWD THEM

DOT PICTURES

THE MAZE

PRETTY TOUGH PUZZLE, EH GANG?
BUT THAT'S BECAUSE YOU DIDN'T
FOLLOW THE DIRECTIONS... BECAUSE
YOU WEREN'T SHARP-WITTED...
BECAUSE YOU DIDN'T GO 'ROUND
THE OUTSIDE AND COME IN
OVER HERE...

WHAT'S WRONG WITH THIS PICTURE?

BETTER STILL YOU SHOULD ASK... WHAT'S *RIGHT*
WITH THIS PICTURE.!!

BACKWORD BY STAN FREBERG

That fortunate legion of us tuned in on the MAD wave length, and therefore receptive to the mighty impulses radiating from its Furshlugginer-active[1] pages, will immediately recognize the wisdom of a Backword. I feel, therefore, that no explanation is necessary. True, a few preoccupied shoppers may whisk the book home thinking it is Norman Vincent Peale or at least "The Mollie Goldberg Cookbook." No matter. These people, being too pseudo-blasé or just plain dull to receive the MAD radiations, will (a) suffer an intense migraine headache four pages in, and (b) fling the book out the window.

So that takes care of *them*.

This leaves a number of non-MAD-addicts who, because of their superior intelligence, will (a) see instantly the brilliant lampoonery that is MAD, (b) curse themselves soundly for having been behind the door when MAD was handed out, and (c) howl all the way through. By the time they will have reached the Backword, their brain-pans will have been conditioned to accept such things without a question. They will have become "MADDICTS" and therefore one of us. And *we* don't need any explanation of a Backword, do we? So the sooner you get it through your potrzebie that there won't be any explanation the better—and that's final now! Crimenentles!

Where was I? Oh, yes, the Backword. For the uninformed, MAD started out three years ago as a comic book kidding only other comic strips. It has graduated today into a first-rate humor magazine, kidding not only comic strips but movies, TV, novels, commercial ads or anything it feels like. Merely to say that I am a fan of this magazine would be like saying that Gina Lollo-

[1] Similar to "radio-active" but with fewer commercials.

183

brigida is "sort of interesting." I am addicted to MAD like the Aga Khan to starches. Why? Because it makes me laugh, and I am rather fond of laughing.

Fortunately, MAD loves to laugh at the same things I do—that is to say, we are both completely insane. MAD does the same thing in a literary (or illiterary) form that I try to do on phonograph records, which is to point up some of the absurdities of mankind through the medium of satire. In a world where things get a shade ridiculous at times, satire is a very important thing to mental health. It lets a little of the air out of people and things who take themselves too seriously and deserve to be brought back down to earth. It also gives everyone a good healthy laugh into the bargain.

MAD is an example of pure and honest satire, written brilliantly by my friend Harvey Kurtzman, and drawn hysterically by Jack Davis, Bill Elder and Wallace Wood. I cannot praise their combined efforts enough. This volume, for example, is taken from several issues of the original MAD and is all written by Harvey. My favorite is "Smilin' Melvin." You may like "Superduperman."[2]

In closing, let us remember that someone once said "Laughter is the best medicine." It is a true fact that a friend of mine had an acquaintance who fell into poor health and proceeded to decline a little each day until the doctors could do nothing for him. Upon being told that the patient was beyond medical help, my friend called one day at his bedside and on a hunch told him a very funny joke he had just heard regarding three wild animals and a man who played the violin.[3] As he reached the punch line, the pale man opened his eyes and laughed for the first time in months. Color returned to his face, and would you believe it?—within forty-eight hours . . . he was dead. The laughter had overtaxed him. This shows how much the guy knew who said "Laughter is the best medicine." HOO HAH!

It is possible, of course, that he meant "Laughter is the best *tasting* medicine." This really shows you what a nudnick he was! I know of some much more daring medicines. I know of a

[2] You may like it but you won't get it, it's in another collection. What do you expect for 35¢ anyway?
[3] This joke is available on request.

cough sirup, for example, that tastes just like Manischewitz Wine when you pour it over the rocks. (It doesn't taste bad over ice, either.) Make this simple test at home: Pour first the cough sirup into a tall glass, then the laughter. See how much of a belt you get out of the laughter! I rest my case.

It seems pointless to go on because I think I have covered the subject adequately, and also because we are running out of paper. Those wishing to read the conclusion of my Backword will find it (with a fine magnifying glass) on the edge of this page in Sanskrit. The body of my message has been put across by now anyhow, which is simply that MAD is my favorite pastime (next to girls) and I hope you have enjoyed INSIDE MAD as much as I did. I boiled mine for dinner.

STAN FREBERG

"WOWEE, GANG— I WISH I'D WRITTEN *BOTH* THESE NEW MAD BOOKS!"

—Charles Dickens

Yes, Charles Dickens of Mazzeppa, Long Island, is just one of thousands who have written in to say they wish they'd written The MAD Reader and MAD Strikes Back!

Now YOU can join the fun! It's easy! Here's how: —run right out to your neighborhood news stand and bring home a copy of The MAD Reader (only 35c). Look it over. Study the pages for the secret clues. Then run right back out to the news stand and buy a copy of MAD Strikes Back! (35c only). Now run right back home again—*fast!* Put the two books side by side and *watch closely.* You will see that they are *two different books!* If they are *three* different books, lie down for a half hour and then try again. On the other hand, if they are two copies of the *same* book it means you haven't been paying attention. We'll go through it one more time, slowly.

1. Run out and buy The MAD Reader (35c).
2. Run out *again* and buy MAD Strikes Back! (Another 35c).

Got it? O.K.—*start running!*

(NOTE: Many fun-loving MAD readers have run out to their local newsdealers and then got lost trying to run back home again. If lost, run to nearest mailbox and send 80c to the publishers, BALLANTINE BOOKS, 404 Fifth Avenue, New York 18, N. Y. They will send you both The MAD Reader and MAD Strikes Back! Of course you will still be lost, but now it will be fun!)

This publication, an exact reprint of Inside MAD *(1955), faithfully reproduces the advertisement above contained in the original. Readers are cautioned against relying on this advertising and should not consider any of it, or offers with it, valid in any way.*

William M. Gaines'

UTTERLY

MAD

™

50TH ANNIVERSARY EDITION

4th Superb Collection!

William M. Gaines'

THE BROTHERS

MAD™

50TH ANNIVERSARY EDITION

5 th Superb Collection!

From ibooks—

The *MAD* Reader
***MAD* Strikes Back!**
Inside *MAD*
Utterly *MAD*
The Brothers *MAD*